PRESENTED BY

# KNIGHT OF ONIONS
## *AND*
# KNIGHT OF GARLIC

# KNIGHT OF ONIONS
## *AND*
# KNIGHT OF GARLIC

### BY HAYYIM NAHMAN BIALIK

TRANSLATED BY HERBERT DANBY
PROFESSOR OF HEBREW, UNIVERSITY OF OXFORD, ENGLAND

ILLUSTRATED BY EMANUEL ROMANO

*NEW YORK*
HEBREW PUBLISHING COMPANY

*Typography by S. A. Jacobs, The Golden Eagle Press,*
*Mount Vernon, N. Y.*
*Printed and bound by Montauk Bookbinding Corp.,*
**New York**

# INTRODUCTORY NOTE

THE *Knight of Onions and Knight of Garlic*, is an elaboration of an anecdote current among the Jews of East Europe. Bialik's Hebrew version is written in short rhyming lines of irregular length and unmetrical, a decorative device very simple to achieve in Hebrew. To have reproduced this in a rhymed English version would have sacrificed the easy fluency, scarcely at all removed from unshackled prose, which marks the original. The device here adopted — unrhymed and not too rigidly regular four-beat lines — preserves approximately the same degree of departure from prose while sacrificing very little in literalness.

H. D.

# KNIGHT OF ONIONS
### *AND*
# KNIGHT OF GARLIC

# KNIGHT OF ONIONS

## *AND*

# KNIGHT OF GARLIC

 PRINCE went forth to roam
the world
And garner knowledge and
experience
As all industrious princes
should.
Through all five continents
he passed,
Through countries old and countries new;
Rivers, lakes and seas he crossed;
He reached the farthest islands' bounds;
He burst beyond mysterious mountains,
Rode through every thirsty steppe.
Ideas he sought in every corner ——

Great or small, it made no matter.
Wise he grew, as wise in fact
As any Socrates or Plato.
Night or day, indoors or out,
He talked as with omniscience
Of things below and things above,
Of things long past and things to come,
Why white was white and black was black,
Why donkeys brayed, why mules were mules,
Why wine surpassed the best of water.

In brief he was, as you have guessed,
An earnest youth and full of worth.

 II

But after fifty days had passed
He thought it time to hie him home:
He seemed no knowledge now to lack;
His sacks and bags were densely crammed
With subtle thoughts in seventy tongues.
He gave command to pack his goods;
When, lo, one came and said to him,

"Good news bring I, most charming Prince!
"Thought I, I will discover it
"Unto his highness: for in truth,
"It is a wondrous, unknown isle.
"Perchance within its treasuries
"Such wisdom hides as still may add
"Unto thy wisdom and renown."
The prince replied,

                "That isle's my goal!"
He hired a ship that day and hour,
Took all his goods, and straight set sail.

He found the isle. But first he felt
A dreary disillusionment:
Naught new he found, except that things
Were somewhat different. Left hands
The islanders bore on the right;
For them today was yesterday,
     And yesterday tomorrow;
Night was day, and day was night;
Squares were round and circles square;

Stairs and trees grew upside down
And people counted backwards way.
It filled the prince with gloom.
    He said,
"Why did I so disturb myself
"To find a land so commonplace?
"That fellow either lied or dreamed!"

While still he stood disconsolate
The people of the isle came down
To greet him; riding, some in litters,
Some on elephants and camels.
Bands of minstrels rode before them
Banging instruments of music
Both with right hand and with left;
Such din must surely penetrate
Throughout the entire universe.
Among the crowds the soldiers pushed
And cried, "Make room!" And so they led
The prince through thronging streets,
    and soon
They reached the royal palace where
A mighty banquet was prepared,
A banquet meet for prince or king.

The island's King received the prince
With hospitality. He filled
With wine a goblet for his guest.
The prince drank deep, and then he saw
How great a feast awaited him:
Meat and fish of every sort,
Fresh-water fish and salty fish,
Fishes short and fishes long,
Fishes known and fishes rare,
Whose coloured juices charmed the eye;
And meats with appetising smell,
Pheasants, quails and pigeons roast
And boiled; and tender calves and fatlings,
Sheep's fat-tail, red heifer's tongue,
Besides choice bread and cakes and wafers,
Honied pancakes, sweetened sponge-cakes,
Cakes with saffron, cakes with raisin;
Not omitting tasty venison,
Hart and roebuck, gazelle and pygarg;
Wines most ancient — from the vats
Which Lot or Noah might have trodden.

King and guest together sat
And ate and drank and waxed replete.

With stomachs stayed both guest and hosts
Sat dozing from satiety
Or sneezing from the incense fumes.
The island's King let forth a sneeze
And politely to his guest remarked,
"Tell me now, my most wise prince,
"If our poor feast was to thy liking."
The prince sneezed too, and courteously
Made answer:
                    "Sire," he said, "I claim
"To be no epicure; but never
"Have I known a feast so sumptuous,
"Fish so choice, or flesh so dainty.
"No lack found I . . . except . . .
        perhaps . . ."
And here the guest began to stutter:
Princely politeness checked his speech.
Expectantly and patiently
The King in silence waited, hoping
Soon to hear the rest. But when
The rest came not, his courtesy failed
And indignation took its place.

In scarce curbed bitterness, he sneered,
"Well what? . . . Go on: 'Except . . .
        perhaps . . .' ?''
The prince evoked his royal tact
To avoid offence, and, sneezing, said,
"Except . . . perhaps . . . it seemed to me
"That such roast meat is much improved
"By one small thing. I had a doubt
"What this might be, and asked my cook,
"And what he said was, 'Eshsh-a . . .
        eshsh-a . . .
" 'esh-shallots' !''

King and nobles all looked blank.
(Such things as onions or shallots
This isle had never seen or known;
No man of them had ever smelt
An onion, peeled or tasted it.)
They thought,
                "Perhaps he merely sneezed."
So they sneezed too, a sneeze wherein
They voiced a wish for information ——
"Eshsh-a? . . . Eshsh-a? . . . Esh-
        shallots?''

The prince knew not that there was aught
That justified astonishment;
So sneezing once, and twice, and thrice,
He emphasised his first remark:
"Eshsh-a ! . . . Eshsh-a ! . . . Esh-
     shallots !"

Still more blank the nobles looked.
The King with hesitance inquired,
"Perhaps, my prince, thou didst but sneeze?
"If otherwise . . . what *are* shallots?"
Scarce had he mouthed this curious word
Than in his nose there came a tick-
     ling ——
So, too, in every noble nose
That graced the royal court —— an itch
That could not be denied, provoked
By fumes of incense, talk of onions.
Noses twisting, stomachs shaking,
King and nobles sneezed in chorus:
"Eshsh-a! . . . Eshsh-a! . . . Esh-
     shallots !"

"Long life to thee!" said prince to King,

"How can it be that such as thou
"Who knowest all earth's lavish gifts
"Dost still not know of what I speak:
"The common, simple, garden onion!
"Scullion, cook and kitchen-maid
"Know every one its piquant reek,
"Its sharpness and its pungency.
"All know its ways while yet it grows
"In garden-bed —— its head below,
"Its legs on high bedecked in bright
"Green pantaloons. Then, ripening,
"It covers up with golden film
"Its fair moist flesh, which all of it
"Is peel on peel, peel on peel,
"Each more tender, till at last
"Its tenderest heart lies bare.
"But O! its flavour! Eaten raw
"It hath no match for bitterness:
"They that taste it cry, 'God help us!'
"They that strip it weep in torrents.
"Poor folk esteem it for its cheapness;
"Others for its quality
"Of rousing ravenous appetite.
"But they who eat it raw to stir

Their hunger, will be well advised
"To nibble at it sparingly;
"For uncurbed onion-eaters foul
"Their mouths and breath with stench
        most noisome.
"But, by thy life! for flav'ring stews
"There's not its peer in all God's works;
"And, roasted with roast meats, its gift
"It is to make them seven times sweeter!
"Such is the rule with this strange plant;
"In life 'tis bitter; in death 'tis sweet.
"If now the King would condescend
"To prove alike my country's fruits
"And my weak words in praise of onions,
"Give but the word. Straightway my cook
"Will make a fire of coals whereon
"To roast a lamb entire, a lamb
"Whose dainty flesh shall end its days
"Festooned with roasted onion shreds.
"And this Elysian dish thus dressed
"Your Majesty's most honoured court
"Shall taste with me this very night.
"For have I not among my wares
"Brought store enough of this fair plant,

"Refreshment for my journey hither?
"Let not the King reject my plea:
"But prove my gift, if it be fair
"And fit for Kings."

His host replied,
"As thou hast spoken, let it be!"

When quiet night beset the town
The King sat down with all his court
To taste the feast for them prepared:
A kid roast whole, likewise a lamb,
Besides a fat and tender hart,
Asleep in golden bubbling fat,
Arrayed in garb of onion shreds,
Reddish brown and scorched with fire,
Glinting, curling, winking, beckoning,
Seducing every jaded palate;
Without a word appealing, winning
Clamorous welcome from all stomachs.
Wines were there, and choicest grapes,
From Cyprus and Aspamia,
Standing priestlike on their platform,
Uttering benediction.

Before the guests could satisfy
Their eyes with what awaited them,
Their nostrils were embraced and charmed
By roasted meat's entrancing smell;
Still more, a raging hunger's torment
Tightly gripped their rumbling bellies.
Wild and famished, with vulture-greed,
Pounced they on the savoury bakemeats,
Rending, tearing, biting, chewing.
No word was said: all saved their strength
To gnaw and masticate and swallow.
Their faces glowed. Into their bones
The luscious fare went down like oil.
Within themselves they vowed. "We'll ne'er
"Retreat till every scrap's licked clean!"
Slick and fast, like mice in traps,
Their Adam's apples jerked, now up
Now down. So hard they laboured,
      teeth,
And jaws and gullets, that great pearls
Of sweat gleamed from their hairless pates;
Till, sighing deep with satisfaction,
One and all gave voice and belched,
"By the Tabernacle's knobs and capitals!

"Met man *ever* tastier victuals?"

His guest's delight the prince beheld.
Then, pouring out a brimming cup
Of red Italian wine, he cried,
"A toast I drink, Long live the King!
"His Majesty hath honoured me
"Before the face of all; and he
"Hath tasted of my country's fruit
"Which hath found favour in his sight.
"And now, perchance, 't would please the King
"To see the jewel of the feast
"In natural form, uncut, uncooked,
"Untouched and raw, as God hath made it.
"At the King's august command
"Forthwith I'll fetch a basketful
"Of golden onions. By thy life,
"O royal Sire! the onion's taste
"Which ye have proved, is not more pleasing
"Than its natural form.  The sight
"Of it will rouse thine eye's desire.
"Then, should it win your Majesty's
"Acceptance, deign to take the gift,
"A memory of my poor self

"And of my country's fruitfulness.
"Then in thy soil may it take root
"And give thee food and boundless pleasure."
The King replied, "Go, fetch it hither!"

 VI

The prince's servant fled in haste
And sought amid the prince's store
Onions large and choice and fair.
He bore them in a golden basket;
And, on the carpet by the royal feet,
He spread them out, a savoury gift.
King and nobles looked in wonder
At the onions, golden coated.
Each took one, and gazed on it.
Never had they seen the like.
They wagged their heads and one to the other
Hissed in whispers, saying,
                              "Who's
"So wise to guess what this may be?"

Among these nobles one there was
Whose bulging paunch vast knowledge held,

Who far excelled all living men
In acumen and quibbles fine.
The onion turned he round and round,
Felt it, squeezed it, once and twice,
Sniffed it thrice with either nostril;
Then he squinted at it closely
Like a doubting diamond broker.
He took two pairs of spectacles
And fixed them tightly on his nose;
Through both he spied; yet, not content,
He made a funnel with his fist
And spied through that.  And next he split
The onion into little pieces.
One by one he shed its wrappings,
Licked it gingerly, and then
Gave forth a slow and cautious verdict:

"This thing combineth in itself
"Bitter with sour and sour with bitter;
"It is somewhat hard yet somewhat soft;
"Its peel is without and likewise within;
"It is not hot nor is it cold,
"Nor wholly dry nor wholly wet;
"Its smell is not like cinnamon,

"Nor doth its taste resemble cummin;
"The radish species cannot claim it;
"It differeth also from the lettuce;
"With incense hath it naught in common.
"Yet were I asked my skilled advice
"I'd say, Its match I've never met
"As titillator for my stomach!"
"God keep thee, Sir!" the prince replied.
"Thou hast convinced me that this land
"Hath none so greatly skilled as thou
"And none with such discerning eye.
"Thine every word is true and clear;
"Thy judgment lucidness itself.
"By thee the onion is laid bare,
"Its deepest secrets now revealed.
"No feeble human eye is thine.
"And blessed be He who gave such wit
"And perspicacity to man!"

 VII

The King (God bless his every deed!)
Most graciously received the gift.

28

He bade his servants guard it well
And keep it packed in myrrh and spices.

He called his seventy councillors
Of whom he asked advice:
                              "How best
"Can we reward this prince, whose gift
"Hath so enriched our island's store?
"What worthy recompense can we
"Bestow that by its rarity
"Shall prove our gratitude and show
"To distant isles that I, your King,
"In generosity excell
"When I requite devoted service?"

Among those seventy councillors
Was one whose baldness and whose fat
Belied a speedy, dart-like mind.
After silent cogitation,
Squeezing tight a bulging brow,
He suddenly called out in joy,

"May God exalt my lord the King!
"A plan have I devised, which straight

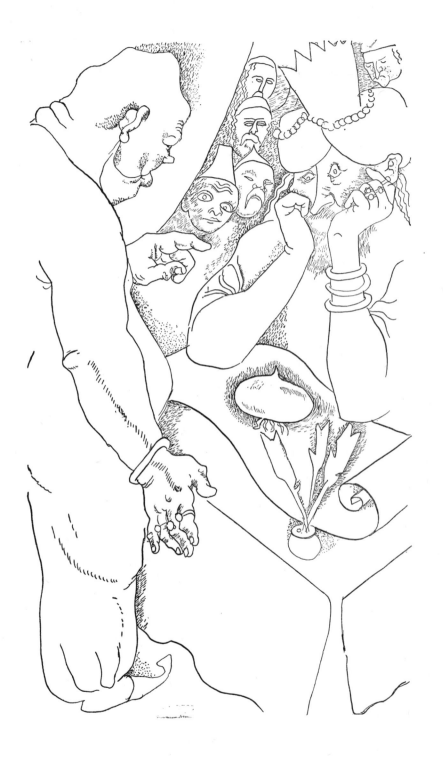

"From heaven into my mind hath sped.
"Inasmuch as this young prince
"(May he live long, a shining light!)
"Hath brought us goodly fruit and new,
"A gift as pleasing as 'tis rare,
"An offering to our lord the King:
"To dole scant honour in return
"Were gross ingratitude — a crime.
"My counsel then is this:
                              "Fill up
"For him with golden coin the basket
"Which with golden onions laden
"He bestowed upon our King.
"And let the King add this thing more:
"A Document, a Charter Royal,
"Wherein the King shall ratify
"This title granted to the prince ——
" 'Exalted Excellence, Knight of Onions!'
"For him in his own country this
"Shall be a sure and faithful proof
"And testimony that he roamed
"The world to good effect, nor ate
"The bread of idleness. So, too,
"For thee, O King, it shall record

"Thy justice and thy favour, proof
"That thou dost honour all who pay
"To thee due honour; and rewardest
"Sevenfold all who do thee service.

"Such is my counsel. And may God
"Preserve the King in peace and health!
"Is not my lord the King as wise
"As any Solomon? And I,
"What am I but a feeble flea
"That liveth but a day, a dog
"Most abject, which is proud to lick
"Its royal master's feet. God bless
"The King, and guard his name and honour!"

This sage advice the King approved
With willing heart. Forthwith
He gave the prince the golden coin
And sealed for him the Charter Royal.
With pomp and honour, and with din
Of drums and instruments of music,
Sailed away the roaming prince
'Exalted Excellence, Knight of Onions!'

## VIII

After certain days (You'll find
The number written down exactly
Even with the hours and minutes
In the Royal Chronicle:
Which is the rule when princes travel) . . .
After certain days, the prince
Returned unto his home with joy;
And twenty pairs of oxen scarce
Sufficed to bear his load of wisdom
And his massed experience.
He made a feast to which he called
The princes in the neighbourhood;
And while they quaffed deep cups of wine
The prince told tales of all the lands
Wherein he'd gathered to himself
Such stores of wisdom. And he told
The tale of his adventures, till
He reached the story of the onions.

And that his honoured guests should know
That truth alone fell from his lips,
He fetched the bag of gold, and there

Before them all he tumbled out
The golden coin that they might see
And handle it and hear its chinking.
So, too, they read and read again
That Charter Royal which proclaimed
The prince's rare nobility ——
"Exalted Excellence, Knight of Onions!"
Never more could any doubt
That he in truth had done great things.
So now his guests, although with wine
Their wits were dulled, extolled his name:
"Exalted Excellence, Knight of Onions!
Praise him for his wondrous works!"

Among the guests a king's son sat,
Whom nobody observed. And that
Was not surprising; for in him
Was naught observable. He had
No beauty, charm, or grace; his flesh
Was meagre. Yet his heart and mind
Were ever watchful and alert.
The story of the onions sank
Deep down within his brain. He saw
In this a challenge to his courage.

"Why," thought he, "if that young prince
"Won gold so cheaply and with ease,
"Why should not I achieve the like?
"I'll put the matter to the proof!"

He planned in secret. Messengers
He sent to ferret out the truth
About this strange and distant island.
After many days' delay
His messengers returned and gave
Him news of comfort and of hope:
"We saw that land, and, lo! throughout
"Its breadth and length *there is no garlic!*
Such was this prince's hope. So when
He heard, he told his plan to none,
But straightway sailed to find that land.

 IX

At length he reached the isle he sought
And then . . . But is there any need
To tell afresh what you have guessed? ——
How, from all the island's people
Found he hearty, noisy welcome;

Whatsoever previously
Befell his brother-prince, the same
Befell him too. Let, then, the reader
Backward turn a page or two,
Read them afresh, and let the weary
Story-teller take his rest.

. . . . . . . . . . . . . . . . . . . . . . . . . . . . . . . .°

. . . . . . . . . . . . . . . . . . . . . . . . . . . . . . .

Then as they dawdled after dinner,
Satiated, talking idly,
Sipping wine and splitting nuts
And chewing raisins and dried figs,
The King in affability
Turned to his guest and said,

                          "We hope,
"O Gracious prince, that thou didst find
"No imperfection in our fare!"
The prince, in answer, deeply bowed:
"All honour to the King!" he said,
"Could any guest perceive a flaw
"In such a royal feast, where all
"The food was dainty, sweet, and pleasing?
"Yet . . . a passing notion struck me
"That, perhaps . . . er . . . ger . . ll . . ck . ."

As a slumberer, waking quickly,
Is both startled and confused,
So the King, surprised, indignant,
Turned upon the prince:
                              "I fail
"To understand! Art thou unwell?
"What didst thou say?"
                              The prince's face
In truth had turned a yellowy-green
From fear lest he had given offence.
"I? What did I say?" he stammered,
"Nothing in particular:
"For who am I that I should dare
"To raise my voice before the King!
"I only mentioned my idea
"That if the cook had introduced
"Into that wondrous roasted dish
"The slightest hint (no more) of garlic,
"Then . . . ah!
"Then its flavour had been perfect!"

Puzzled still, the King inquired,
"What *was* that word thou saidst? Gar . . gar . . . ?"
The nobles, too, showed their surprise

For none of them had heard or seen,
Still less had smelt or tasted garlic:
None was known in all that isle.
The prince resolved to waste no words.
His servants sent he in all haste
To fetch the pungent plant. They brought
A hamper filled with garlic choice
And poured it out in one small heap
Before the King and courtiers.
They gazed on it, they handled **it,**
They all cried out in wonder,

                            "Look!

"O! look upon its belly, see
"Its legs, its whiskers and moustache!
"Praise God who hath created it!"
The King looked round and caught the eye
Of his most shrewd and famed magician,
One whose nose was paved with warts
And pimply corrugations; one
Whose lightest words were oracles.
From off the heap he took a fine
And comely root with whiskers full
And belly fine. Upon his hand
He laid it gently like a baby

In its cot. He scrutinised it
Up and down; he felt its head
And fumbled gently with its whiskers,
Seven times stroking leg and belly.
This was not enough for him:
He pulled it piecemeal into bits
And with his thumbnail stripped a rib
And left it bare as on the day
When it was born, disclosing it
In all its perfect purity,
In colour like a precious pearl
Or milky tooth immaculate . . .
. . . . . . . . . . . . . . . . . . . . . . . . . . . . . . .

Swift it sped . . . that virgin whiff !
The King's magician, shocked and gasping,
Wildly clutching means defensive,
Stuffed both nostrils tight with snuff
And blinked and sneezed and found relief.
Then turning to the King he said,
"God save the King and raise his honour
"High as Hermon ! May his savour
"Sweet as flowing myrrh be wafted
"Like the scents from Lebanon !
"And who am I — a puny ass,

"A snail that melteth into slime ——

"That I should dare to lay my thoughts

"Before the King? But, caught within

"My feeble mesh of understanding,

"Thus the matter lies:

                          "This plant,

"As I perceive it, is naught else

"Than younger brother or relation

"To that precious fruit, the onion.

"Both alike, O King and nobles,

"Clothe themselves in countless cloaks;

"And though this fruit the smaller be

"Yet God hath ample compensation

"Given in potency and worth.

"It hath a comelier grace within,

"Its colour is more delicate,

"Its milk-white flesh more fair and pure.

"With beard and hairy head 't is blessed;

"And though its outer garb lacks much

"In splendour, 't is not just to judge

"By outward signs alone. God's ways

"Are not as man's: Some times there are

"When what, within, is passing fair,

"Without, hath naught of comeliness.

"

"Moreover, judging by my nose
"(and mine discernment doth not lack)
"The lesser one by far excels
"In sharpness and acridity
"Its prouder, finer-coated brother.
"In short, despite their difference,
"Their family is one. To sight
"They seem distinct; but one great law
"And quality embraceth both:
"Their sharp and stimulating stench!

"Such is the sum of my research.
"What I have learnt I have revealed
"Unto my lord the King; and naught
"Have I concealed, but duly served
"His Majesty with faithful heart."

 X

Urgently the royal word
Went forth to test this savour new.
A clove of garlic, gently rubbed
Within the cooking-pot wherein

45

Was roast a young and tender kid,
Lent such aroma to the fare
As left no doubt that what the prince
Had claimed for garlic's bounty erred
(If err it did) by understatement.
Never (so they all agreed)
Had nose or palate known such bliss
As that which garlic freely gave;
And when the King had had his fill
Of roasted kid made sweeter far
By garlic's matchless benediction,
Youthful vigour pouring richly
Through his marrow, made his bones
Rejoice; while as for that most shrewd
And famed magician, every pimple
Scintillated on his nose
Like piles of brightly crimson corals.
Thus the words of wisdom written
Black on white by ancient sages
Were fulfilled, in that they said,
"Ten virtues garlic giveth them
"That eat it: glistening face, and eyes
"That shine, and entrails purged of worms"
(And as for you who'd know the rest,

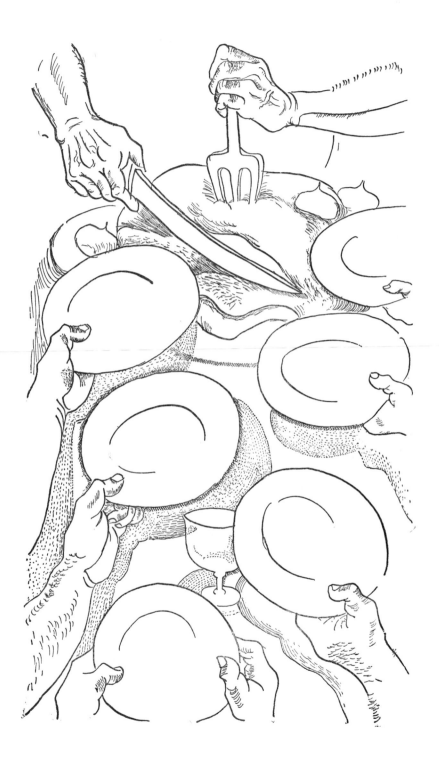

We think you'd better search and find
And read the passage for yourselves.)

Without delay, that selfsame night,
The seventy councillors of the King
And all his sagest courtiers
Were called to sit in robes of state
In solemn session to decide
What form the royal gratitude
Should take, and how before the world
The King could show most fittingly
His august pleasure in this prince,
This man of garlic, generous guest,
Who had endowed the island's soil
With one more boon from Nature's store.
"Your prudent counsel," said the King,
"I now require, that all mankind
"May learn that goodly recompense
"Unfailing, followeth goodly deeds."

Like hens which sit and brood in hope
Of hatching out some sprightly chick,
The elders sat with frowning brows
In cogitation deep. They stroked

Their well trimmed hoary beards; they scratched
Their hairless shiny skulls. They strove
To find some picturesque requital,
Something which must please the prince
Without a faintest hint of doubt
And satisfy his dearest wish,
And likewise match in rarity,
In aptness and in quality,
The prince's lavish gift; so, too,
It must be such that would make known
In every land from sea to sea,
From East to West, the glorious pride
And honour of this island's King.

Their cogitations slowly dragged:
Hard toil it was, the elders found,
To hatch an egg so perfect. Then,
Like one awakening out of slumber,
Up there rose the pimply- nosed
Magician:
            "Gentleman," cried he,
"Why all this heavy cogitation?
"Why this hesitating doubt?
"Never was there a problem whose

"Solution was more manifest!
" 'Tis true: a precious thing the prince
"Hath given our isle. But have we not
"Already one great treasure, prized
"Most highly, closely kept, without
"Its equal anywhere on earth?
"What act more generous, more befitting,
"Can we meditate than this ——
"To give that treasure as reward
"And compensation for the garlic?
"Thus we pay our debt in full;
"Thus, too, the honour of our King,
"His wealth and generosity,
"Shine clear before the world; thus, too,
"Without a doubt, our princely guest
"Will find contentment. So, my lords,
"Our answer to the question which
"His Majesty hath deigned to put,
"It is none other than . . . an onion!"

With loud applause the elders heard
This simple and most apt solution.

## XI

After two days more, the bells
Rang out, and every man and woman
In that island, from the highest
To the lowest in the land,
From King and Queen and councillors
To kitchen-maid and chimney-sweep,
Rushed out into the streets to speed
The princely guest and honour him
With clamorous shouts, with thundering drums,
With cymbals and with whirling dance,
To prove how fervent was this island's
Gratitude towards their guest.
Through thronging, dense and cheering crowds
The prince processed towards the shore,
While every knee before him bowed.
He rode in lone and gloomy splendour
On a tall and tawny ass.
Behind him came the island's chieftains,
Seventy men on seventy steeds,
And after them the lesser captains
With the island's men-at-arms.
Before the prince, on soft pads treading,

Gaily decked, like any bride,
Walked a haughty camel, led
By cameleer of high degree;
And on her hump a precious load
She bore — the royal gift to him
Who rode behind, the parting guest,
The hero of the hour.
                              Within
A silken, gilt embroidered bag
Was honourably packed a large
And solid onion; furthermore
Appended to this silken bag
There hung a parchment scroll, a Charter
Royal, skilfully inscribed,
Bedecked and cunningly illumined
By the King's own scrivener,
Wherein 'twas written, signed and sealed
By Royal Signet: "By These Presents
"Know that thee We have created
" 'Knight of Garlic' ". And the Royal
Heralds trumpeted and shouted
"Thus the King is pleased to honour
"All whose service findeth favour!"
And the people shouted all,

"Long live the Prince! Hail! Knight of
        Garlic!
"Health to him and prosperous voyage!"

Every bell in every tower
Pealed in chorus. Every flag
Was waved. And women on the housetops
Crowned their heads with onion-wreaths
And onions showered on folk below.
And all this time the cymbals crashed
And drums boomed forth in thunderous roar.

The prince came home. But of his going
Or returning, told he nothing.
Shamefully he hid in silence,
Clothed in deep humility.